MW00439287

Fit and Food

JOURNAL

www.youcanteatlove.com

Facebook: You Can't Eat Love

Copyright Page:

Fit and Food Journal © Copyright 2020 Leslie Lindsey Davis

All rights reserved. No part of this publication may be reproduced, distributed or transmitted in any form or by any means, including photocopying, recording, or other electronic or mechanical methods, without the prior written permission of the publisher, except in the case of brief quotations embodied in critical reviews and certain other noncommercial uses permitted by copyright law. Although the author and publisher have made every effort to ensure that the information in this book was correct at press time, the author and publisher do not assume and hereby disclaim any liability to any party for any loss, damage, or disruption caused by errors or omissions, whether such errors or omissions result from negligence, accident, or any other cause. Adherence to all applicable laws and regulations, including international, federal, state and local governing professional licensing, business practices, advertising, and all other aspects of doing business in the US, Canada or any other jurisdiction is the sole responsibility of the reader and consumer. Neither the author nor the publisher assumes any responsibility or liability whatsoever on behalf of the consumer or reader of this material. Any perceived slight of any individual or organization is purely unintentional. The resources in this book are provided for informational purposes only and should not be used to replace the specialized training and professional judgment of a health care or mental health care professional. Neither the author nor the publisher can be held responsible for the use of the information provided within this book. Please always consult a trained professional before making any decision regarding treatment of yourself or others.

For more
information, email leslie@youcanteatlove.com
ISBN: 9781736232200
(print only)

How to Use
Fit and Food Journal

Welcome!
Congratulations on taking care of yourself!

You will find 2 places to record the following information –

➡ Before and After the six weeks:

- Body measurements
- Current weight and
- Any other information that you might want to remember
- Photo

(Suggestion - create an album on your phone or computer where you can put your selfie shots. This will help you see how your body is changing.)

➡ The next pages are about your WHY. Your WHY is what will get you to the gym when your bed or the TV are calling you. Your WHY is what will help you make healthier food choices. Don't cheat yourself by skipping this part.

➡ And finally:

- Suggested exercises to get you started.
- Fit pages begin in the front (right after all this information)
- Food pages begin from the back.
- You have six weeks of Fit and Food tracking.
- Fill out your results page. Don't forget the photo!
- Reminder to reorder
- Private Facebook page for community

Celebrate taking care of you!

Where Am I Now

Date

Weight

Height

Body Fat %

Before Photo

Measurments

Neck

Chest

Bicep (Upper Arm)

Waist

Hips

Thigh

Calf

Results

Date

Weight

Height

Body Fat %

After Photo

Measurments

Neck

Chest

Bicep (Upper Arm)

Waist

Hips

Thigh

Calf

<u>Finding you so you can discover your why:</u>

1.   What excites you (think about things you like to do; places you like to go)

   _____

   _____

2.   On a scale of 1-5 rate how you feel about the following areas of your life (1 is extremely unhappy, 5 is extremely happy) – Health, Friends, Family, Recreation, Personal Growth
   Health _____ Friends _____ Family _____
   Recreation (Fun) _____ Personal Growth _____

3.   Now write *why* you gave each of those areas the rating you did. Be honest. Remember, no one else is going to see this unless you decide to share.
   Health

   _____

   _____

   Friends_____

   _____

   Family

   _____

   _____

   Recreation (Fun)

   _____

   _____

   Personal
   Growth_____

   _____

4. What do you *believe* you can't do (and yes, losing weight or heavy lifting can be one of the things)

   _____

   _____

5. What would your life look like if you believed you *could* do those things? (Channel the *Little Engine that Could* if you need to.)

   _____

   _____

6. Ten years ago, what was your relationship with food and exercise.

   _____

   _____

7. Today, what is your relationship with food and exercise – what changed? Why do you think it changed?

   _____

   _____

8. What are your fears (list as many as you can think of and failure can be one of those fears. So can success.)? I'm afraid of

   _____

   because_____
   (Keep going! You've got this!-Get extra paper if needed)

   _____

   _____

   _____

9. Pick one of your fears and think about how it would feel to act against just that one fear. What would that look like?

_____

_____

_____

10. List the challenges you've had over the past year.

_____

_____

_____

_____

11. What did you learn about yourself from these challenges?

_____

_____

_____

_____

12. My long-time mantra is I don't want to be 80 years old, sitting on my front porch in my rocker saying I wish I would have (and then I would fill in the blank) – now your turn:

_____

_____

_____

_____

_____

_____

Fill in these blanks: My name is

_____

I'm (not a job title or diet/exercise failure)

_____.

In the past I have (had what kind of relationship/belief system about food/exercise)

_____

_____

but now I'm ready to (describe what kind of relationship you want with yourself)

_____

_____

and it's important to me because (nothing to do with your weight/ability, another person or an event)

_____

_____

Why I want to reclaim myself matters. I'm important to me.

Welcome to your WHY!

(Copy your WHY so you can keep it to remind yourself WHY you are going to the gym and WHY you are making healthy choices)

EXERCISES TO TARGET SPECIFIC MUSCLES (FRONT)

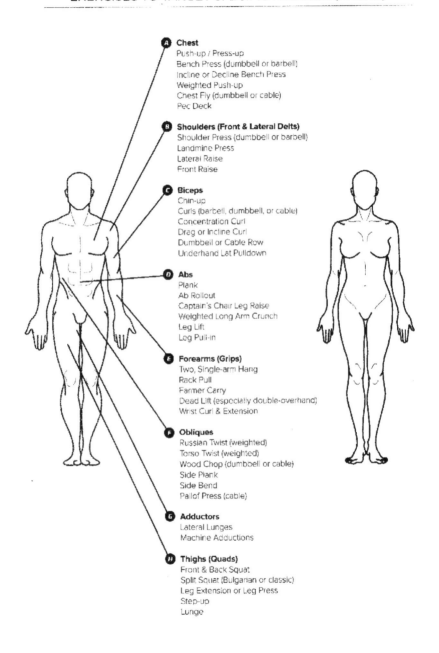

A Chest
Push-up / Press-up
Bench Press (dumbbell or barbell)
Incline or Decline Bench Press
Weighted Push-up
Chest Fly (dumbbell or cable)
Pec Deck

B Shoulders (Front & Lateral Delts)
Shoulder Press (dumbbell or barbell)
Landmine Press
Lateral Raise
Front Raise

C Biceps
Chin-up
Curls (barbell, dumbbell, or cable)
Concentration Curl
Drag or Incline Curl
Dumbbell or Cable Row
Underhand Lat Pulldown

D Abs
Plank
Ab Rollout
Captain's Chair Leg Raise
Weighted Long Arm Crunch
Leg Lift
Leg Pull-in

E Forearms (Grips)
Two, Single-arm Hang
Rack Pull
Farmer Carry
Dead Lift (especially double-overhand)
Wrist Curl & Extension

F Obliques
Russian Twist (weighted)
Torso Twist (weighted)
Wood Chop (dumbbell or cable)
Side Plank
Side Bend
Pallof Press (cable)

G Adductors
Lateral Lunges
Machine Adductions

H Thighs (Quads)
Front & Back Squat
Split Squat (Bulgarian or classic)
Leg Extension or Leg Press
Step-up
Lunge

EXERCISES TO TARGET SPECIFIC MUSCLES (BACK)

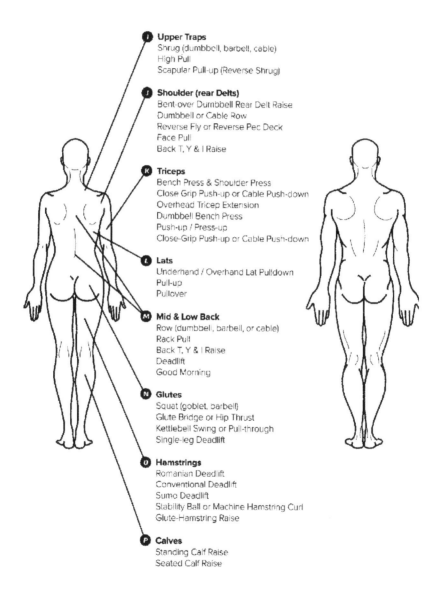

I Upper Traps
Shrug (dumbbell, barbell, cable)
High Pull
Scapular Pull-up (Reverse Shrug)

J Shoulder (rear Delts)
Bent-over Dumbbell Rear Delt Raise
Dumbbell or Cable Row
Reverse Fly or Reverse Pec Deck
Face Pull
Back T, Y & I Raise

K Triceps
Bench Press & Shoulder Press
Close Grip Push-up or Cable Push-down
Overhead Tricep Extension
Dumbbell Bench Press
Push-up / Press-up
Close-Grip Push-up or Cable Push-down

L Lats
Underhand / Overhand Lat Pulldown
Pull-up
Pullover

M Mid & Low Back
Row (dumbbell, barbell, or cable)
Rack Pull
Back T, Y & I Raise
Deadlift
Good Morning

N Glutes
Squat (goblet, barbell)
Glute Bridge or Hip Thrust
Kettlebell Swing or Pull-through
Single-leg Deadlift

O Hamstrings
Romanian Deadlift
Conventional Deadlift
Sumo Deadlift
Stability Ball or Machine Hamstring Curl
Glute-Hamstring Raise

P Calves
Standing Calf Raise
Seated Calf Raise

Take care of your body, its the only place you have to live.

JIM ROHN

Fit

Week 1

MY GOAL FOR THE WEEK

HOW I AM GOING TO CELEBRATE

Jan   Feb   Mar   Apr   May   June   July   Aug   Sep   Oct   Nov   Dec
1 2 3 4 5 6 7 8 9 10 11 12 13 14 15 16 17 18 19 20 21 22 23 24 25 26 27 28 29 30 31

Goal for Today _____

Muscle Group		Stretch ____			Warm-up ____		
Exercise		Set 1	Set 2	Set 3	Set 4	Set 5	Set 6
	Reps						
	Lbs						

Cardio   Time   Intensity/Speed   Notes _____

_____   _____

Cool-Down ____

Goal for Next Workout _____

Questions for Trainer _____

Jan Feb Mar Apr May June July Aug Sep Oct Nov Dec
1 2 3 4 5 6 7 8 9 10 11 12 13 14 15 16 17 18 19 20 21 22 23 24 25 26 27 28 29 30 31

Goal for Today _____

Muscle Group		Stretch ___			Warm-up ___		
Exercise		Set 1	Set 2	Set 3	Set 4	Set 5	Set 6
	Reps						
	Lbs						

Cardio   Time Intensity/Speed   Notes _____

_____   _____

Cool-Down ___   _____

Goal for Next Workout _____

Questions for Trainer _____

_____

Jan   Feb   Mar   Apr   May   June   July   Aug   Sep   Oct   Nov   Dec
1 2 3 4 5 6 7 8 9 10 11 12 13 14 15 16 17 18 19 20 21 22 23 24 25 26 27 28 29 30 31

Goal for Today _____

Muscle Group	Stretch ___			Warm-up ___		
Exercise	Set 1	Set 2	Set 3	Set 4	Set 5	Set 6
Reps						
Lbs						

Cardio   Time   Intensity/Speed   Notes _____

_____   _____

Cool-Down ___

Goal for Next Workout _____

Questions for Trainer _____

_____

Jan Feb Mar Apr May June July Aug Sep Oct Nov Dec
1 2 3 4 5 6 7 8 9 10 11 12 13 14 15 16 17 18 19 20 21 22 23 24 25 26 27 28 29 30 31

Goal for Today _____

Muscle Group	Stretch ___			Warm-up ___		
Exercise	Set 1	Set 2	Set 3	Set 4	Set 5	Set 6
Reps						
Lbs						

Cardio   Time Intensity/Speed   Notes _____

_____   _____

Cool-Down ___   _____

Goal for Next Workout _____

Questions for Trainer _____

Jan Feb Mar Apr May June July Aug Sep Oct Nov Dec

1 2 3 4 5 6 7 8 9 10 11 12 13 14 15 16 17 18 19 20 21 22 23 24 25 26 27 28 29 30 31

Goal for Today _____

Muscle Group	Stretch ____			Warm-up ____		
Exercise	Set 1	Set 2	Set 3	Set 4	Set 5	Set 6
Reps						
Lbs						

Cardio   Time Intensity/Speed   Notes _____

_____   _____

Cool-Down ____

Goal for Next Workout _____

Questions for Trainer _____

Jan Feb Mar Apr May June July Aug Sep Oct Nov Dec
1 2 3 4 5 6 7 8 9 10 11 12 13 14 15 16 17 18 19 20 21 22 23 24 25 26 27 28 29 30 31

Goal for Today _____

Muscle Group	Stretch ___			Warm-up ___		
Exercise	Set 1	Set 2	Set 3	Set 4	Set 5	Set 6
Reps						
Lbs						

Cardio   Time Intensity/Speed   Notes _____

_____   _____

Cool-Down ___

Goal for Next Workout _____

Questions for Trainer _____

Jan Feb Mar Apr May June July Aug Sep Oct Nov Dec
1 2 3 4 5 6 7 8 9 10 11 12 13 14 15 16 17 18 19 20 21 22 23 24 25 26 27 28 29 30 31

Goal for Today _____

Muscle Group		Stretch ____			Warm-up ____		
Exercise		Set 1	Set 2	Set 3	Set 4	Set 5	Set 6
	Reps						
	Lbs						

Cardio   Time Intensity/Speed   Notes _____

_____   _____

Cool-Down ____   _____

Goal for Next Workout _____

Questions for Trainer _____

_____

Reflecting on my week

We don't need to be perfect... we just need to get started.

UNKNOWN

Week 2

MY GOAL FOR THE WEEK

HOW I AM GOING TO CELEBRATE

Jan   Feb   Mar   Apr   May   June   July   Aug   Sep   Oct   Nov   Dec
1 2 3 4 5 6 7 8 9 10 11 12 13 14 15 16 17 18 19 20 21 22 23 24 25 26 27 28 29 30 31

Goal for Today _____

Muscle Group		Stretch ____			Warm-up ____		
Exercise		Set 1	Set 2	Set 3	Set 4	Set 5	Set 6
	Reps						
	Lbs						

Cardio   Time   Intensity/Speed   Notes _____

_____   _____

Cool-Down ____   _____

Goal for Next Workout _____

Questions for Trainer _____

_____

Jan   Feb   Mar   Apr   May   June   July   Aug   Sep   Oct   Nov   Dec
1 2 3 4 5 6 7 8 9 10 11 12 13 14 15 16 17 18 19 20 21 22 23 24 25 26 27 28 29 30 31

Goal for Today _____

Muscle Group		Stretch ____			Warm-up ____		
Exercise		Set 1	Set 2	Set 3	Set 4	Set 5	Set 6
	Reps						
	Lbs						

Cardio	Time	Intensity/Speed	Notes _____

_____   _____

Cool-Down ____

Goal for Next Workout _____

Questions for Trainer _____

Jan Feb Mar Apr May June July Aug Sep Oct Nov Dec
1 2 3 4 5 6 7 8 9 10 11 12 13 14 15 16 17 18 19 20 21 22 23 24 25 26 27 28 29 30 31

Goal for Today _____

Muscle Group	Stretch ___			Warm-up ___		
Exercise	Set 1	Set 2	Set 3	Set 4	Set 5	Set 6
Reps						
Lbs						

Cardio	Time	Intensity/Speed	Notes _____

_____   _____

Cool-Down ___   _____

Goal for Next Workout _____

Questions for Trainer _____

_____

Jan Feb Mar Apr May June July Aug Sep Oct Nov Dec
1 2 3 4 5 6 7 8 9 10 11 12 13 14 15 16 17 18 19 20 21 22 23 24 25 26 27 28 29 30 31

Goal for Today _____

Muscle Group		Stretch ___			Warm-up ___		
Exercise		Set 1	Set 2	Set 3	Set 4	Set 5	Set 6
	Reps						
	Lbs						

Cardio   Time Intensity/Speed   Notes _____

_____   _____

Cool-Down ___

Goal for Next Workout _____

Questions for Trainer _____

Jan Feb Mar Apr May June July Aug Sep Oct Nov Dec
1 2 3 4 5 6 7 8 9 10 11 12 13 14 15 16 17 18 19 20 21 22 23 24 25 26 27 28 29 30 31

Goal for Today _____

Muscle Group	Stretch ___			Warm-up ___		
Exercise	Set 1	Set 2	Set 3	Set 4	Set 5	Set 6
Reps						
Lbs						

Cardio   Time Intensity/Speed   Notes _____

_____   _____

Cool-Down ___   _____

Goal for Next Workout _____

Questions for Trainer _____

_____

Jan Feb Mar Apr May June July Aug Sep Oct Nov Dec
1 2 3 4 5 6 7 8 9 10 11 12 13 14 15 16 17 18 19 20 21 22 23 24 25 26 27 28 29 30 31

Goal for Today _____

Muscle Group		Stretch ___			Warm-up ___		
Exercise		Set 1	Set 2	Set 3	Set 4	Set 5	Set 6
	Reps						
	Lbs						

Cardio _____ Time Intensity/Speed   Notes _____

_____   _____

Cool-Down ___   _____

Goal for Next Workout _____

Questions for Trainer _____

_____

Jan Feb Mar Apr May June July Aug Sep Oct Nov Dec
1 2 3 4 5 6 7 8 9 10 11 12 13 14 15 16 17 18 19 20 21 22 23 24 25 26 27 28 29 30 31

Goal for Today _____

Muscle Group	Stretch ___			Warm-up ___		
Exercise	Set 1	Set 2	Set 3	Set 4	Set 5	Set 6
Reps						
Lbs						

Cardio   Time Intensity/Speed   Notes _____

_____   _____

Cool-Down ____   _____

Goal for Next Workout _____

Questions for Trainer _____

_____

Reflecting on my week

It never gets easier. You just get better at it.

JORDAN HOECHLIN

Week 3

MY GOAL FOR THE WEEK

HOW I AM GOING TO CELEBRATE

Jan Feb Mar Apr May June July Aug Sep Oct Nov Dec
1 2 3 4 5 6 7 8 9 10 11 12 13 14 15 16 17 18 19 20 21 22 23 24 25 26 27 28 29 30 31

Goal for Today _____

Muscle Group	Stretch ___			Warm-up ___		
Exercise	Set 1	Set 2	Set 3	Set 4	Set 5	Set 6
Reps						
Lbs						

Cardio   Time Intensity/Speed   Notes _____

_____   _____

Cool-Down ___

Goal for Next Workout _____

Questions for Trainer _____

Jan Feb Mar Apr May June July Aug Sep Oct Nov Dec
1 2 3 4 5 6 7 8 9 10 11 12 13 14 15 16 17 18 19 20 21 22 23 24 25 26 27 28 29 30 31

Goal for Today _____

Muscle Group		Stretch ___			Warm-up ___		
Exercise		Set 1	Set 2	Set 3	Set 4	Set 5	Set 6
	Reps						
	Lbs						

Cardio   Time Intensity/Speed   Notes _____

_____   _____

Cool-Down ___   _____

Goal for Next Workout _____

                      _____

Questions for Trainer _____

                      _____

Jan Feb Mar Apr May June July Aug Sep Oct Nov Dec
1 2 3 4 5 6 7 8 9 10 11 12 13 14 15 16 17 18 19 20 21 22 23 24 25 26 27 28 29 30 31

Goal for Today _____

Muscle Group	Stretch ____			Warm-up ____		
Exercise	Set 1	Set 2	Set 3	Set 4	Set 5	Set 6
Reps						
Lbs						

Cardio   Time Intensity/Speed   Notes _____

_____   _____

Cool-Down ____   _____

Goal for Next Workout _____

Questions for Trainer _____

_____

Jan Feb Mar Apr May June July Aug Sep Oct Nov Dec
1 2 3 4 5 6 7 8 9 10 11 12 13 14 15 16 17 18 19 20 21 22 23 24 25 26 27 28 29 30 31

Goal for Today _____

Muscle Group		Stretch ____			Warm-up ____		
Exercise		Set 1	Set 2	Set 3	Set 4	Set 5	Set 6
	Reps						
	Lbs						

| Cardio | Time | Intensity/Speed | Notes _____ |

Cool-Down ____

Goal for Next Workout _____

Questions for Trainer _____

Jan Feb Mar Apr May June July Aug Sep Oct Nov Dec
1 2 3 4 5 6 7 8 9 10 11 12 13 14 15 16 17 18 19 20 21 22 23 24 25 26 27 28 29 30 31

Goal for Today _____

Muscle Group	Stretch ____			Warm-up ____		
Exercise	Set 1	Set 2	Set 3	Set 4	Set 5	Set 6
Reps						
Lbs						

Cardio   Time Intensity/Speed   Notes _____

_____   _____

Cool-Down ____   _____

Goal for Next Workout _____

Questions for Trainer _____

_____

Jan Feb Mar Apr May June July Aug Sep Oct Nov Dec
1 2 3 4 5 6 7 8 9 10 11 12 13 14 15 16 17 18 19 20 21 22 23 24 25 26 27 28 29 30 31

Goal for Today _____

Muscle Group		Stretch ____			Warm-up ____		
Exercise		Set 1	Set 2	Set 3	Set 4	Set 5	Set 6
	Reps						
	Lbs						

Cardio	Time	Intensity/Speed	Notes _____

_____   _____

Cool-Down ____   _____

Goal for Next Workout _____

Questions for Trainer _____
                      _____

Jan Feb Mar Apr May June July Aug Sep Oct Nov Dec
1 2 3 4 5 6 7 8 9 10 11 12 13 14 15 16 17 18 19 20 21 22 23 24 25 26 27 28 29 30 31

Goal for Today _____

Muscle Group		Stretch ____			Warm-up ____		
Exercise		Set 1	Set 2	Set 3	Set 4	Set 5	Set 6
	Reps						
	Lbs						

Cardio   Time Intensity/Speed   Notes _____

_____   _____

Cool-Down ____   _____

Goal for Next Workout _____

Questions for Trainer _____

_____

Reflecting on my week

The same voice that says "give up" can also be trained to say "keep going".

UNKNOWN

Week 4

MY GOAL FOR THE WEEK

HOW I AM GOING TO CELEBRATE

Jan Feb Mar Apr May June July Aug Sep Oct Nov Dec
1 2 3 4 5 6 7 8 9 10 11 12 13 14 15 16 17 18 19 20 21 22 23 24 25 26 27 28 29 30 31

Goal for Today _____

Muscle Group		Stretch ____			Warm-up ____		
Exercise		Set 1	Set 2	Set 3	Set 4	Set 5	Set 6
	Reps						
	Lbs						

Cardio   Time Intensity/Speed   Notes _____

_____   _____

Cool-Down ____   _____

Goal for Next Workout _____

                                    _____

Questions for Trainer _____

                                    _____

Jan Feb Mar Apr May June July Aug Sep Oct Nov Dec
1 2 3 4 5 6 7 8 9 10 11 12 13 14 15 16 17 18 19 20 21 22 23 24 25 26 27 28 29 30 31

Goal for Today _____

Muscle Group		Stretch ___			Warm-up ___		
Exercise		Set 1	Set 2	Set 3	Set 4	Set 5	Set 6
	Reps						
	Lbs						

Cardio   Time Intensity/Speed   Notes _____

_____   _____

Cool-Down ___   _____

Goal for Next Workout _____

Questions for Trainer _____

_____

Jan   Feb   Mar   Apr   May   June   July   Aug   Sep   Oct   Nov   Dec
1 2 3 4 5 6 7 8 9 10 11 12 13 14 15 16 17 18 19 20 21 22 23 24 25 26 27 28 29 30 31

Goal for Today _____

| Muscle Group | Stretch ____ | | | Warm-up ____ | | |
Exercise	Set 1	Set 2	Set 3	Set 4	Set 5	Set 6
Reps						
Lbs						

Cardio   Time   Intensity/Speed   Notes _____

_____   _____

Cool-Down ____   _____

Goal for Next Workout _____

Questions for Trainer _____

_____

Jan   Feb   Mar   Apr   May   June   July   Aug   Sep   Oct   Nov   Dec
1 2 3 4 5 6 7 8 9 10 11 12 13 14 15 16 17 18 19 20 21 22 23 24 25 26 27 28 29 30 31

Goal for Today _____

Muscle Group		Stretch ____			Warm-up ____		
Exercise		Set 1	Set 2	Set 3	Set 4	Set 5	Set 6
	Reps						
	Lbs						

Cardio	Time	Intensity/Speed	Notes _____

_____

Cool-Down ____

Goal for Next Workout _____

Questions for Trainer _____

_____

Jan   Feb   Mar   Apr   May   June   July   Aug   Sep   Oct   Nov   Dec
1 2 3 4 5 6 7 8 9 10 11 12 13 14 15 16 17 18 19 20 21 22 23 24 25 26 27 28 29 30 31

Goal for Today _____

Muscle Group	Stretch ____			Warm-up ____		
Exercise	Set 1	Set 2	Set 3	Set 4	Set 5	Set 6
Reps						
Lbs						

Cardio _____ Time _____ Intensity/Speed _____   Notes _____

_____   _____

Cool-Down ____

Goal for Next Workout _____

Questions for Trainer _____

_____

Jan Feb Mar Apr May June July Aug Sep Oct Nov Dec
1 2 3 4 5 6 7 8 9 10 11 12 13 14 15 16 17 18 19 20 21 22 23 24 25 26 27 28 29 30 31

Goal for Today _____

Muscle Group	Stretch ____			Warm-up ____		
Exercise	Set 1	Set 2	Set 3	Set 4	Set 5	Set 6
Reps						
Lbs						

Cardio   Time Intensity/Speed   Notes _____

_____   _____

Cool-Down ____   _____

Goal for Next Workout _____

Questions for Trainer _____

Jan Feb Mar Apr May June July Aug Sep Oct Nov Dec
1 2 3 4 5 6 7 8 9 10 11 12 13 14 15 16 17 18 19 20 21 22 23 24 25 26 27 28 29 30 31

Goal for Today _____

Muscle Group		Stretch ____			Warm-up ____		
Exercise		Set 1	Set 2	Set 3	Set 4	Set 5	Set 6
	Reps						
	Lbs						

Cardio   Time Intensity/Speed   Notes _____

_____   _____

Cool-Down ____   _____

Goal for Next Workout   _____

Questions for Trainer   _____

_____

Reflecting on my week

Have a purpose and you won't need motivation.

UNKNOWN

Week 5

MY GOAL FOR THE WEEK

HOW I AM GOING TO CELEBRATE

Jan Feb Mar Apr May June July Aug Sep Oct Nov Dec
1 2 3 4 5 6 7 8 9 10 11 12 13 14 15 16 17 18 19 20 21 22 23 24 25 26 27 28 29 30 31

Goal for Today _____

Muscle Group	Stretch ____			Warm-up ____		
Exercise	Set 1	Set 2	Set 3	Set 4	Set 5	Set 6
Reps						
Lbs						

Cardio   Time Intensity/Speed   Notes _____

_____   _____

Cool-Down ____   _____

Goal for Next Workout _____

Questions for Trainer _____

Jan Feb Mar Apr May June July Aug Sep Oct Nov Dec

1 2 3 4 5 6 7 8 9 10 11 12 13 14 15 16 17 18 19 20 21 22 23 24 25 26 27 28 29 30 31

Goal for Today _____

Muscle Group		Stretch ___			Warm-up ___		
Exercise		Set 1	Set 2	Set 3	Set 4	Set 5	Set 6
	Reps						
	Lbs						

Cardio	Time	Intensity/Speed	Notes _____

_____   _____

Cool-Down ___

Goal for Next Workout _____

Questions for Trainer _____
_____

Jan Feb Mar Apr May June July Aug Sep Oct Nov Dec
1 2 3 4 5 6 7 8 9 10 11 12 13 14 15 16 17 18 19 20 21 22 23 24 25 26 27 28 29 30 31

Goal for Today _____

Muscle Group		Stretch ____			Warm-up ____		
Exercise		Set 1	Set 2	Set 3	Set 4	Set 5	Set 6
	Reps						
	Lbs						

Cardio   Time Intensity/Speed   Notes _____

_____   _____

Cool-Down ____   _____

Goal for Next Workout _____

Questions for Trainer _____

_____

Jan Feb Mar Apr May June July Aug Sep Oct Nov Dec
1 2 3 4 5 6 7 8 9 10 11 12 13 14 15 16 17 18 19 20 21 22 23 24 25 26 27 28 29 30 31

Goal for Today _____

Muscle Group	Stretch ____			Warm-up ____		
Exercise	Set 1	Set 2	Set 3	Set 4	Set 5	Set 6
Reps						
Lbs						

Cardio	Time	Intensity/Speed	Notes

Cool-Down ____

Goal for Next Workout _____

Questions for Trainer _____

Jan Feb Mar Apr May June July Aug Sep Oct Nov Dec
1 2 3 4 5 6 7 8 9 10 11 12 13 14 15 16 17 18 19 20 21 22 23 24 25 26 27 28 29 30 31

Goal for Today _____

Muscle Group		Stretch ____			Warm-up ____		
Exercise		Set 1	Set 2	Set 3	Set 4	Set 5	Set 6
	Reps						
	Lbs						

Cardio   Time Intensity/Speed   Notes _____

_____   _____

Cool-Down ____   _____

Goal for Next Workout _____

                                          _____
Questions for Trainer _____

                                          _____

Jan Feb Mar Apr May June July Aug Sep Oct Nov Dec
1 2 3 4 5 6 7 8 9 10 11 12 13 14 15 16 17 18 19 20 21 22 23 24 25 26 27 28 29 30 31

Goal for Today _____

Muscle Group		Stretch ___			Warm-up ___		
Exercise		Set 1	Set 2	Set 3	Set 4	Set 5	Set 6
	Reps						
	Lbs						

Cardio _____ Time Intensity/Speed   Notes _____

_____   _____

Cool-Down ____   _____

Goal for Next Workout _____

Questions for Trainer _____

_____

Jan Feb Mar Apr May June July Aug Sep Oct Nov Dec
1 2 3 4 5 6 7 8 9 10 11 12 13 14 15 16 17 18 19 20 21 22 23 24 25 26 27 28 29 30 31

Goal for Today _____

Muscle Group		Stretch ____			Warm-up ____		
Exercise		Set 1	Set 2	Set 3	Set 4	Set 5	Set 6
	Reps						
	Lbs						

Cardio _____ Time ____ Intensity/Speed ____   Notes _____

_____   _____

Cool-Down ____   _____

Goal for Next Workout _____

Questions for Trainer _____

_____

Reflecting on my week

Each day is another chance to change your life.

UNKNOWN

Week 6

MY GOAL FOR THE WEEK

HOW I AM GOING TO CELEBRATE

Jan Feb Mar Apr May June July Aug Sep Oct Nov Dec
1 2 3 4 5 6 7 8 9 10 11 12 13 14 15 16 17 18 19 20 21 22 23 24 25 26 27 28 29 30 31

Goal for Today _____

| Muscle Group | Stretch ___ | | | Warm-up ___ | | |
Exercise	Set 1	Set 2	Set 3	Set 4	Set 5	Set 6
Reps						
Lbs						

Cardio   Time Intensity/Speed   Notes _____

_____   _____

Cool-Down ____   _____

Goal for Next Workout _____

Questions for Trainer _____

Jan   Feb   Mar   Apr   May   June   July   Aug   Sep   Oct   Nov   Dec
1 2 3 4 5 6 7 8 9 10 11 12 13 14 15 16 17 18 19 20 21 22 23 24 25 26 27 28 29 30 31

Goal for Today _____

Muscle Group		Stretch ____			Warm-up ____		
Exercise		Set 1	Set 2	Set 3	Set 4	Set 5	Set 6
	Reps						
	Lbs						

Cardio   Time   Intensity/Speed   Notes _____

_____   _____

Cool-Down ____   _____

Goal for Next Workout _____

Questions for Trainer _____

Jan Feb Mar Apr May June July Aug Sep Oct Nov Dec
1 2 3 4 5 6 7 8 9 10 11 12 13 14 15 16 17 18 19 20 21 22 23 24 25 26 27 28 29 30 31

Goal for Today _____

Muscle Group	Stretch ___			Warm-up ___		
Exercise	Set 1	Set 2	Set 3	Set 4	Set 5	Set 6
Reps						
Lbs						

Cardio _____ Time ___ Intensity/Speed ___ Notes _____

Cool-Down ___

Goal for Next Workout _____

Questions for Trainer _____

Jan Feb Mar Apr May June July Aug Sep Oct Nov Dec
1 2 3 4 5 6 7 8 9 10 11 12 13 14 15 16 17 18 19 20 21 22 23 24 25 26 27 28 29 30 31

Goal for Today _____

Muscle Group	Stretch ____			Warm-up ____		
Exercise	Set 1	Set 2	Set 3	Set 4	Set 5	Set 6
Reps						
Lbs						

Cardio   Time Intensity/Speed   Notes _____

_____   _____

Cool-Down ____   _____

Goal for Next Workout _____

Questions for Trainer _____

_____

Jan   Feb   Mar   Apr   May   June   July   Aug   Sep   Oct   Nov   Dec
1 2 3 4 5 6 7 8 9 10 11 12 13 14 15 16 17 18 19 20 21 22 23 24 25 26 27 28 29 30 31

Goal for Today _____

Muscle Group	Stretch ____			Warm-up ____		
Exercise	Set 1	Set 2	Set 3	Set 4	Set 5	Set 6
Reps						
Lbs						

Cardio _____   Time Intensity/Speed   Notes _____

_____   _____

Cool-Down ____   _____

Goal for Next Workout _____

Questions for Trainer _____

_____

Jan   Feb   Mar   Apr   May   June   July   Aug   Sep   Oct   Nov   Dec
1 2 3 4 5 6 7 8 9 10 11 12 13 14 15 16 17 18 19 20 21 22 23 24 25 26 27 28 29 30 31

Goal for Today _____

Muscle Group	Stretch ____			Warm-up ____		
Exercise	Set 1	Set 2	Set 3	Set 4	Set 5	Set 6
Reps						
Lbs						

Cardio   Time   Intensity/Speed   Notes _____

_____   _____

Cool-Down ____   _____

Goal for Next Workout   _____

                             _____

Questions for Trainer   _____

                             _____

Jan   Feb   Mar   Apr   May   June   July   Aug   Sep   Oct   Nov   Dec
1 2 3 4 5 6 7 8 9 10 11 12 13 14 15 16 17 18 19 20 21 22 23 24 25 26 27 28 29 30 31

Goal for Today _____

Muscle Group		Stretch ____			Warm-up ____		
Exercise		Set 1	Set 2	Set 3	Set 4	Set 5	Set 6
	Reps						
	Lbs						

Cardio   Time   Intensity/Speed   Notes _____

_____   _____

Cool-Down ____   _____

Goal for Next Workout _____

Questions for Trainer _____

Reflecting on my week

Nothing changes if nothing changes.

COURTNEY C STEVENS

Fit

Food

Once you believe in yourself, and you put your mind to something, you can do it.

SIMONE BILES

Reflecting on my week

Jan Feb Mar Apr May June July Aug Sep Oct Nov Dec
1 2 3 4 5 6 7 8 9 10 11 12 13 14 15 16 17 18 19 20 21 22 23 24 25 26 27 28 29 30 31

Goal for Today ....

Food Log	Calories		Protein (g)		Carbs (g)	
	Target ____		Target ____		Target ____	
	Count	Remaining	Count	Remaining	Count	Remaining

You doing ok?   ☹ ☺ ☺ ☹

Tell me about it... ....

Goal for tomorrow ....

Nutrient Tracker

of Servings   Recommended

Water		
Grains		6 to 8
Veggies		3 to 5
Fruits		2 to 4
Dairy		2 to 3
Protein		3 to 4
Fats	Sugars	Moderation

Jan   Feb   Mar   Apr   May   June   July   Aug   Sep   Oct   Nov   Dec
1 2 3 4 5 6 7 8 9 10 11 12 13 14 15 16 17 18 19 20 21 22 23 24 25 26 27 28 29 30 31

Goal for Today _____

Food Log	Calories		Protein (g)		Carbs (g)	
	Target ____		Target ____		Target ____	
	Count	Remaining	Count	Remaining	Count	Remaining

You doing ok?   ☺ ☺ ☺ ☹

Tell me about it... ....

Goal for tomorrow _____

Nutrient Tracker

of Servings   Recommended

Water		
Grains		6 to 8
Veggies		3 to 5
Fruits		2 to 4
Dairy		2 to 3
Protein		3 to 4
Fats	Sugars	Moderation

Jan Feb Mar Apr May June July Aug Sep Oct Nov Dec
1 2 3 4 5 6 7 8 9 10 11 12 13 14 15 16 17 18 19 20 21 22 23 24 25 26 27 28 29 30 31

Goal for Today ....

Food Log	Calories		Protein (g)		Carbs (g)	
	Target ____		Target ____		Target ____	
	Count	Remaining	Count	Remaining	Count	Remaining

You doing ok?   ☺ ☺ ☺ ☹

Tell me about it... ....
....
....

Goal for tomorrow ....

Nutrient Tracker

of Servings   Recommended

Water		
Grains		6 to 8
Veggies		3 to 5
Fruits		2 to 4
Dairy		2 to 3
Protein		3 to 4
Fats	Sugars	Moderation

Jan   Feb   Mar   Apr   May   June   July   Aug   Sep   Oct   Nov   Dec
1 2 3 4 5 6 7 8 9 10 11 12 13 14 15 16 17 18 19 20 21 22 23 24 25 26 27 28 29 30 31

Goal for Today _____

Food Log	Calories		Protein (g)		Carbs (g)	
	Target ____		Target ____		Target ____	
	Count	Remaining	Count	Remaining	Count	Remaining

You doing ok?   ☺   ☺   ☺   ☹

Tell me about it.... _____

_____

Goal for tomorrow _____

Nutrient Tracker

of Servings   Recommended

Water		
Grains		6 to 8
Veggies		3 to 5
Fruits		2 to 4
Dairy		2 to 3
Protein		3 to 4
Fats	Sugars	Moderation

Jan Feb Mar Apr May June July Aug Sep Oct Nov Dec
1 2 3 4 5 6 7 8 9 10 11 12 13 14 15 16 17 18 19 20 21 22 23 24 25 26 27 28 29 30 31

Goal for Today ....

Food Log	Calories		Protein (g)		Carbs (g)	
	Target _____		Target _____		Target _____	
	Count	Remaining	Count	Remaining	Count	Remaining

You doing ok?   ☺   ☺   ☺   ☹

Tell me about it.... ....

....

....

Goal for tomorrow ....

Nutrient Tracker

of Servings   Recommended

			Recommended
Water			
Grains			6 to 8
Veggies			3 to 5
Fruits			2 to 4
Dairy			2 to 3
Protein			3 to 4
Fats		Sugars	Moderation

Jan   Feb   Mar   Apr   May   June   July   Aug   Sep   Oct   Nov   Dec
1 2 3 4 5 6 7 8 9 10 11 12 13 14 15 16 17 18 19 20 21 22 23 24 25 26 27 28 29 30 31

Goal for Today ....

Food Log	Calories		Protein (g)		Carbs (g)	
	Target ____		Target ____		Target ____	
	Count	Remaining	Count	Remaining	Count	Remaining

You doing ok?   ☺   ☺   ☹   ☹

Tell me about it.... ....
....
....
....

Goal for tomorrow ....

Nutrient Tracker

of Servings   Recommended

Water		
Grains		6 to 8
Veggies		3 to 5
Fruits		2 to 4
Dairy		2 to 3
Protein		3 to 4
Fats	Sugars	Moderation

Jan Feb Mar Apr May June July Aug Sep Oct Nov Dec
1 2 3 4 5 6 7 8 9 10 11 12 13 14 15 16 17 18 19 20 21 22 23 24 25 26 27 28 29 30 31

Goal for Today ....

Food Log	Calories		Protein (g)		Carbs (g)	
	Target ____		Target ____		Target ____	
	Count	Remaining	Count	Remaining	Count	Remaining

You doing ok? ☺ ☺ ☺ ☹

Tell me about it... ....

....

....

Goal for tomorrow ....

Nutrient Tracker

of Servings   Recommended

Water		
Grains		6 to 8
Veggies		3 to 5
Fruits		2 to 4
Dairy		2 to 3
Protein		3 to 4
Fats	Sugars	Moderation

Reflecting on my week

Jan Feb Mar Apr May June July Aug Sep Oct Nov Dec
1 2 3 4 5 6 7 8 9 10 11 12 13 14 15 16 17 18 19 20 21 22 23 24 25 26 27 28 29 30 31

Goal for Today _____

Food Log	Calories Target ____		Protein (g) Target ____		Carbs (g) Target ____	
	Count	Remaining	Count	Remaining	Count	Remaining

You doing ok?   😊   🙂   😐   🙁

Tell me about it... _____

_____

_____

Goal for tomorrow _____

Nutrient Tracker

of Servings   Recommended

Water		
Grains		6 to 8
Veggies		3 to 5
Fruits		2 to 4
Dairy		2 to 3
Protein		3 to 4
Fats	Sugars	Moderation

Jan Feb Mar Apr May June July Aug Sep Oct Nov Dec
1 2 3 4 5 6 7 8 9 10 11 12 13 14 15 16 17 18 19 20 21 22 23 24 25 26 27 28 29 30 31

Goal for Today _____

Food Log	Calories		Protein (g)		Carbs (g)	
	Target ____		Target ____		Target ____	
	Count	Remaining	Count	Remaining	Count	Remaining

You doing ok?   ☺ ☺ ☺ ☹

Tell me about it.... _____

_____

Goal for tomorrow   _____

Nutrient Tracker

of Servings   Recommended

Water		
Grains		6 to 8
Veggies		3 to 5
Fruits		2 to 4
Dairy		2 to 3
Protein		3 to 4
Fats	Sugars	Moderation

Jan Feb Mar Apr May June July Aug Sep Oct Nov Dec
1 2 3 4 5 6 7 8 9 10 11 12 13 14 15 16 17 18 19 20 21 22 23 24 25 26 27 28 29 30 31

Goal for Today ....

Food Log	Calories Target ____		Protein (g) Target ____		Carbs (g) Target ____	
	Count	Remaining	Count	Remaining	Count	Remaining

You doing ok?   ☺   ☺   ☺   ☹

Tell me about it... ....
....
....
....

Goal for tomorrow ....

Nutrient Tracker

of Servings   Recommended

Water	
Grains	6 to 8
Veggies	3 to 5
Fruits	2 to 4
Dairy	2 to 3
Protein	3 to 4
Fats	Sugars Moderation

Jan Feb Mar Apr May June July Aug Sep Oct Nov Dec
1 2 3 4 5 6 7 8 9 10 11 12 13 14 15 16 17 18 19 20 21 22 23 24 25 26 27 28 29 30 31

Goal for Today ....

Food Log	Calories Target ____		Protein (g) Target ____		Carbs (g) Target ____	
	Count	Remaining	Count	Remaining	Count	Remaining

You doing ok?   ☺   ☺   ☺   ☹

Tell me about it.... ....

....

....

Goal for tomorrow

Nutrient Tracker

of Servings   Recommended

Water		
Grains		6 to 8
Veggies		3 to 5
Fruits		2 to 4
Dairy		2 to 3
Protein		3 to 4
Fats	Sugars	Moderation

Jan Feb Mar Apr May June July Aug Sep Oct Nov Dec
1 2 3 4 5 6 7 8 9 10 11 12 13 14 15 16 17 18 19 20 21 22 23 24 25 26 27 28 29 30 31

Goal for Today

Food Log	Calories		Protein (g)		Carbs (g)	
	Target ____		Target ____		Target ____	
	Count	Remaining	Count	Remaining	Count	Remaining

You doing ok?   ☺ ☺ ☺ ☹

Tell me about it...

Goal for tomorrow

Nutrient Tracker

of Servings   Recommended

Water		
Grains		6 to 8
Veggies		3 to 5
Fruits		2 to 4
Dairy		2 to 3
Protein		3 to 4
Fats	Sugars	Moderation

Jan   Feb   Mar   Apr   May   June   July   Aug   Sep   Oct   Nov   Dec
1 2 3 4 5 6 7 8 9 10 11 12 13 14 15 16 17 18 19 20 21 22 23 24 25 26 27 28 29 30 31

Goal for Today _____

Food Log	Calories		Protein (g)		Carbs (g)	
	Target ____		Target ____		Target ____	
	Count	Remaining	Count	Remaining	Count	Remaining

You doing ok?   😵   🙂   😐   🙁

Tell me about it.... _____
_____
_____

Goal for tomorrow _____

Nutrient Tracker

of Servings   Recommended

Water		
Grains		6 to 8
Veggies		3 to 5
Fruits		2 to 4
Dairy		2 to 3
Protein		3 to 4
Fats	Sugars	Moderation

Jan Feb Mar Apr May June July Aug Sep Oct Nov Dec
1 2 3 4 5 6 7 8 9 10 11 12 13 14 15 16 17 18 19 20 21 22 23 24 25 26 27 28 29 30 31

Goal for Today _____

Food Log	Calories		Protein (g)		Carbs (g)	
	Target ____		Target ____		Target ____	
	Count	Remaining	Count	Remaining	Count	Remaining

You doing ok?   ☺ ☺ ☺ ☹

Tell me about it... ....
....
....
Goal for tomorrow ....

Nutrient Tracker

of Servings   Recommended

Water		
Grains		6 to 8
Veggies		3 to 5
Fruits		2 to 4
Dairy		2 to 3
Protein		3 to 4
Fats	Sugars	Moderation

Week 6

MY GOAL FOR THE WEEK

_____

HOW I AM GOING TO CELEBRATE

_____

Time to reorder!
https://www.amazon.com/dp/1736232207

Everything you need is within you.

SHALANE FLANAGAN

Reflecting on my week

Jan Feb Mar Apr May June July Aug Sep Oct Nov Dec
1 2 3 4 5 6 7 8 9 10 11 12 13 14 15 16 17 18 19 20 21 22 23 24 25 26 27 28 29 30 31

Goal for Today

Food Log	Calories		Protein (g)		Carbs (g)	
	Target ____		Target ____		Target ____	
	Count	Remaining	Count	Remaining	Count	Remaining

You doing ok?   ☺ ☺ ☹ ☹

Tell me about it...

Goal for tomorrow

Nutrient Tracker

of Servings   Recommended

Water		
Grains		6 to 8
Veggies		3 to 5
Fruits		2 to 4
Dairy		2 to 3
Protein		3 to 4
Fats	Sugars	Moderation

Jan Feb Mar Apr May June July Aug Sep Oct Nov Dec
1 2 3 4 5 6 7 8 9 10 11 12 13 14 15 16 17 18 19 20 21 22 23 24 25 26 27 28 29 30 31

Goal for Today _____

Food Log	Calories		Protein (g)		Carbs (g)	
	Target ___		Target ___		Target ___	
	Count	Remaining	Count	Remaining	Count	Remaining

You doing ok?   ☺ ☺ ☺ ☹

Tell me about it.... ....

....

Goal for tomorrow ....

Nutrient Tracker

of Servings   Recommended

		Recommended
Water		
Grains		6 to 8
Veggies		3 to 5
Fruits		2 to 4
Dairy		2 to 3
Protein		3 to 4
Fats	Sugars	Moderation

Jan   Feb   Mar   Apr   May   June   July   Aug   Sep   Oct   Nov   Dec
1 2 3 4 5 6 7 8 9 10 11 12 13 14 15 16 17 18 19 20 21 22 23 24 25 26 27 28 29 30 31

Goal for Today ....

Food Log	Calories		Protein (g)		Carbs (g)	
	Target ____		Target ____		Target ____	
	Count	Remaining	Count	Remaining	Count	Remaining

You doing ok?   ☺   ☺   ☹   ☹

Tell me about it... ....
....
....

Goal for tomorrow ....

Nutrient Tracker

of Servings   Recommended

Water		
Grains		6 to 8
Veggies		3 to 5
Fruits		2 to 4
Dairy		2 to 3
Protein		3 to 4
Fats	Sugars	Moderation

Jan   Feb   Mar   Apr   May   June   July   Aug   Sep   Oct   Nov   Dec
1 2 3 4 5 6 7 8 9 10 11 12 13 14 15 16 17 18 19 20 21 22 23 24 25 26 27 28 29 30 31

Goal for Today _____

Food Log	Calories		Protein (g)		Carbs (g)	
	Target ____		Target ____		Target ____	
	Count	Remaining	Count	Remaining	Count	Remaining

You doing ok?   ☺ ☺ ☺ ☹

Tell me about it.... _____
_____
_____

Goal for tomorrow _____

Nutrient Tracker

of Servings   Recommended

Water		
Grains		6 to 8
Veggies		3 to 5
Fruits		2 to 4
Dairy		2 to 3
Protein		3 to 4
Fats	Sugars	Moderation

Jan Feb Mar Apr May June July Aug Sep Oct Nov Dec
1 2 3 4 5 6 7 8 9 10 11 12 13 14 15 16 17 18 19 20 21 22 23 24 25 26 27 28 29 30 31

Goal for Today _____

Food Log	Calories		Protein (g)		Carbs (g)	
	Target ____		Target ____		Target ____	
	Count	Remaining	Count	Remaining	Count	Remaining

You doing ok?   ☺ ☺ ☺ ☹

Tell me about it... _____
_____
_____

Goal for tomorrow _____

Nutrient Tracker

of Servings   Recommended

Water		
Grains		6 to 8
Veggies		3 to 5
Fruits		2 to 4
Dairy		2 to 3
Protein		3 to 4
Fats	Sugars	Moderation

Jan Feb Mar Apr May June July Aug Sep Oct Nov Dec
1 2 3 4 5 6 7 8 9 10 11 12 13 14 15 16 17 18 19 20 21 22 23 24 25 26 27 28 29 30 31

Goal for Today _____

Food Log	Calories		Protein (g)		Carbs (g)	
	Target _____		Target _____		Target _____	
	Count	Remaining	Count	Remaining	Count	Remaining

You doing ok?   ☺ ☺ ☺ ☹

Tell me about it... ....

_____
_____

Goal for tomorrow _____

Nutrient Tracker

of Servings   Recommended

Water		
Grains		6 to 8
Veggies		3 to 5
Fruits		2 to 4
Dairy		2 to 3
Protein		3 to 4
Fats	Sugars	Moderation

Jan Feb Mar Apr May June July Aug Sep Oct Nov Dec
1 2 3 4 5 6 7 8 9 10 11 12 13 14 15 16 17 18 19 20 21 22 23 24 25 26 27 28 29 30 31

Goal for Today ....

Food Log	Calories		Protein (g)		Carbs (g)	
	Target ____		Target ____		Target ____	
	Count	Remaining	Count	Remaining	Count	Remaining

You doing ok?   ☺ ☺ ☹ ☹

Tell me about it.... ....

....

....

Goal for tomorrow ....

Nutrient Tracker

of Servings   Recommended

Water		
Grains		6 to 8
Veggies		3 to 5
Fruits		2 to 4
Dairy		2 to 3
Protein		3 to 4
Fats	Sugars	Moderation

Week 5

MY GOAL FOR THE WEEK

HOW I AM GOING TO CELEBRATE

Time to reorder!
https://www.amazon.com/dp/1736232207

I've failed over
and over again in
my life. And that is
why I succeed.

MICHAEL JORDAN

Reflecting on my week

Jan   Feb   Mar   Apr   May   June   July   Aug   Sep   Oct   Nov   Dec
1 2 3 4 5 6 7 8 9 10 11 12 13 14 15 16 17 18 19 20 21 22 23 24 25 26 27 28 29 30 31

Goal for Today ....

Food Log	Calories		Protein (g)		Carbs (g)	
	Target ____		Target ____		Target ____	
	Count	Remaining	Count	Remaining	Count	Remaining

You doing ok?   ☺   ☺   ☺   ☹

Tell me about it... ....

Goal for tomorrow ....

Nutrient Tracker

of Servings   Recommended

Water
Grains   6 to 8
Veggies   3 to 5
Fruits   2 to 4
Dairy   2 to 3
Protein   3 to 4
Fats   Sugars   Moderation

Jan Feb Mar Apr May June July Aug Sep Oct Nov Dec
1 2 3 4 5 6 7 8 9 10 11 12 13 14 15 16 17 18 19 20 21 22 23 24 25 26 27 28 29 30 31

Goal for Today _____

Food Log	Calories		Protein (g)		Carbs (g)	
	Target ____		Target ____		Target ____	
	Count	Remaining	Count	Remaining	Count	Remaining

You doing ok?   ☺ ☺ ☹ ☹

Tell me about it.... _____

_____

_____

Goal for tomorrow _____

Nutrient Tracker

of Servings   Recommended

Water		
Grains		6 to 8
Veggies		3 to 5
Fruits		2 to 4
Dairy		2 to 3
Protein		3 to 4
Fats	Sugars	Moderation

Jan Feb Mar Apr May June July Aug Sep Oct Nov Dec
1 2 3 4 5 6 7 8 9 10 11 12 13 14 15 16 17 18 19 20 21 22 23 24 25 26 27 28 29 30 31

Goal for Today _____

Food Log	Calories Target ____		Protein (g) Target ____		Carbs (g) Target ____	
	Count	Remaining	Count	Remaining	Count	Remaining

You doing ok? ☺ ☺ ☺ ☹

Tell me about it... ....
_____
_____

Goal for tomorrow _____

Nutrient Tracker

of Servings

		Recommended
Water		
Grains		6 to 8
Veggies		3 to 5
Fruits		2 to 4
Dairy		2 to 3
Protein		3 to 4
Fats	Sugars	Moderation

Jan Feb Mar Apr May June July Aug Sep Oct Nov Dec
1 2 3 4 5 6 7 8 9 10 11 12 13 14 15 16 17 18 19 20 21 22 23 24 25 26 27 28 29 30 31

Goal for Today _____

Food Log	Calories Target ____		Protein (g) Target ____		Carbs (g) Target ____	
	Count	Remaining	Count	Remaining	Count	Remaining

You doing ok?   ☺   ☺   ☺   ☹

Tell me about it.... ....

Goal for tomorrow   _____

Nutrient Tracker

of Servings   Recommended

Water		
Grains		6 to 8
Veggies		3 to 5
Fruits		2 to 4
Dairy		2 to 3
Protein		3 to 4
Fats	Sugars	Moderation

Jan Feb Mar Apr May June July Aug Sep Oct Nov Dec
1 2 3 4 5 6 7 8 9 10 11 12 13 14 15 16 17 18 19 20 21 22 23 24 25 26 27 28 29 30 31

Goal for Today

Food Log	Calories		Protein (g)		Carbs (g)	
	Target _____		Target _____		Target _____	
	Count	Remaining	Count	Remaining	Count	Remaining

You doing ok?   ☺ ☺ ☺ ☹

Tell me about it...

Goal for tomorrow

Nutrient Tracker

of Servings   Recommended

Water		
Grains		6 to 8
Veggies		3 to 5
Fruits		2 to 4
Dairy		2 to 3
Protein		3 to 4
Fats	Sugars	Moderation

Jan Feb Mar Apr May June July Aug Sep Oct Nov Dec
1 2 3 4 5 6 7 8 9 10 11 12 13 14 15 16 17 18 19 20 21 22 23 24 25 26 27 28 29 30 31

Goal for Today _____

Food Log	Calories		Protein (g)		Carbs (g)	
	Target ____		Target ____		Target ____	
	Count	Remaining	Count	Remaining	Count	Remaining

You doing ok? 😊 🙂 😕 🙁

Tell me about it.... _____
_____
_____

Goal for tomorrow _____

Nutrient Tracker

of Servings   Recommended

Water		
Grains		6 to 8
Veggies		3 to 5
Fruits		2 to 4
Dairy		2 to 3
Protein		3 to 4
Fats	Sugars	Moderation

Jan   Feb   Mar   Apr   May   June   July   Aug   Sep   Oct   Nov   Dec
1 2 3 4 5 6 7 8 9 10 11 12 13 14 15 16 17 18 19 20 21 22 23 24 25 26 27 28 29 30 31

Goal for Today ....

Food Log	Calories		Protein (g)		Carbs (g)	
	Target ____		Target ____		Target ____	
	Count	Remaining	Count	Remaining	Count	Remaining

You doing ok?   ☺   ☺   ☺   ☹

Tell me about it... ....

Goal for tomorrow ....

Nutrient Tracker

of Servings   Recommended

Water		
Grains		6 to 8
Veggies		3 to 5
Fruits		2 to 4
Dairy		2 to 3
Protein		3 to 4
Fats	Sugars	Moderation

Week 4

MY GOAL FOR THE WEEK

HOW I AM GOING TO CELEBRATE

It's ok to struggle, but it's not ok to give up on yourself or your dreams.

GABE GRUNEWALD

Reflecting on my week

Jan   Feb   Mar   Apr   May   June   July   Aug   Sep   Oct   Nov   Dec
1 2 3 4 5 6 7 8 9 10 11 12 13 14 15 16 17 18 19 20 21 22 23 24 25 26 27 28 29 30 31

Goal for Today

Food Log	Calories		Protein (g)		Carbs (g)	
	Target _____		Target _____		Target _____	
	Count	Remaining	Count	Remaining	Count	Remaining

You doing ok?   ☺   ☺   ☺   ☹

Tell me about it...

Goal for tomorrow

Nutrient Tracker

of Servings   Recommended

Water		
Grains		6 to 8
Veggies		3 to 5
Fruits		2 to 4
Dairy		2 to 3
Protein		3 to 4
Fats	Sugars	Moderation

Jan   Feb   Mar   Apr   May   June   July   Aug   Sep   Oct   Nov   Dec
1 2 3 4 5 6 7 8 9 10 11 12 13 14 15 16 17 18 19 20 21 22 23 24 25 26 27 28 29 30 31

Goal for Today ....

Food Log	Calories		Protein (g)		Carbs (g)	
	Target _____		Target _____		Target _____	
	Count	Remaining	Count	Remaining	Count	Remaining

You doing ok?   ☺   ☺   ☺   ☹

Tell me about it.... ....
....
....

Goal for tomorrow ....

Nutrient Tracker

of Servings   Recommended

Water		
Grains		6 to 8
Veggies		3 to 5
Fruits		2 to 4
Dairy		2 to 3
Protein		3 to 4
Fats	Sugars	Moderation

Jan Feb Mar Apr May June July Aug Sep Oct Nov Dec
1 2 3 4 5 6 7 8 9 10 11 12 13 14 15 16 17 18 19 20 21 22 23 24 25 26 27 28 29 30 31

Goal for Today _____

Food Log	Calories		Protein (g)		Carbs (g)	
	Target ____		Target ____		Target ____	
	Count	Remaining	Count	Remaining	Count	Remaining

You doing ok?   ☺ ☺ ☺ ☹

Tell me about it... ....
_____
_____

Goal for tomorrow _____

Nutrient Tracker

of Servings   Recommended

Water
Grains   6 to 8
Veggies   3 to 5
Fruits   2 to 4
Dairy   2 to 3
Protein   3 to 4
Fats   Sugars   Moderation

Jan   Feb   Mar   Apr   May   June   July   Aug   Sep   Oct   Nov   Dec
1 2 3 4 5 6 7 8 9 10 11 12 13 14 15 16 17 18 19 20 21 22 23 24 25 26 27 28 29 30 31

Goal for Today _____

Food Log	Calories		Protein (g)		Carbs (g)	
	Target ____		Target ____		Target ____	
	Count	Remaining	Count	Remaining	Count	Remaining

You doing ok?   ☺   ☺   ☺   ☹

Tell me about it.... ....

_____

_____

Goal for tomorrow _____

Nutrient Tracker

of Servings   Recommended

Water		
Grains		6 to 8
Veggies		3 to 5
Fruits		2 to 4
Dairy		2 to 3
Protein		3 to 4
Fats	Sugars	Moderation

Jan Feb Mar Apr May June July Aug Sep Oct Nov Dec
1 2 3 4 5 6 7 8 9 10 11 12 13 14 15 16 17 18 19 20 21 22 23 24 25 26 27 28 29 30 31

Goal for Today

Food Log	Calories		Protein (g)		Carbs (g)	
	Target ____		Target ____		Target ____	
	Count	Remaining	Count	Remaining	Count	Remaining

You doing ok? ☺ ☺ ☺ ☹

Tell me about it...

Goal for tomorrow

Nutrient Tracker

of Servings   Recommended

Water		
Grains		6 to 8
Veggies		3 to 5
Fruits		2 to 4
Dairy		2 to 3
Protein		3 to 4
Fats	Sugars	Moderation

Jan Feb Mar Apr May June July Aug Sep Oct Nov Dec
1 2 3 4 5 6 7 8 9 10 11 12 13 14 15 16 17 18 19 20 21 22 23 24 25 26 27 28 29 30 31

Goal for Today _____

Food Log	Calories Target _____		Protein (g) Target _____		Carbs (g) Target _____	
	Count	Remaining	Count	Remaining	Count	Remaining

You doing ok?   ☺ ☺ ☹ ☹

Tell me about it.... _____
_____
_____

Goal for tomorrow _____

Nutrient Tracker

of Servings   Recommended

Water	
Grains	6 to 8
Veggies	3 to 5
Fruits	2 to 4
Dairy	2 to 3
Protein	3 to 4
Fats Sugars	Moderation

Jan Feb Mar Apr May June July Aug Sep Oct Nov Dec
1 2 3 4 5 6 7 8 9 10 11 12 13 14 15 16 17 18 19 20 21 22 23 24 25 26 27 28 29 30 31

Goal for Today _____

Food Log	Calories		Protein (g)		Carbs (g)	
	Target ____		Target ____		Target ____	
	Count	Remaining	Count	Remaining	Count	Remaining

You doing ok? ☺ ☺ ☹ ☹

Tell me about it... ....
....
....

Goal for tomorrow ....

Nutrient Tracker

of Servings   Recommended

Water		
Grains		6 to 8
Veggies		3 to 5
Fruits		2 to 4
Dairy		2 to 3
Protein		3 to 4
Fats	Sugars	Moderation

Week 3

MY GOAL FOR THE WEEK

HOW I AM GOING TO CELEBRATE

It's never too late to change old habits.

FLORENCE GRIFFITH JOYNER

Reflecting on my week

Jan   Feb   Mar   Apr   May   June   July   Aug   Sep   Oct   Nov   Dec
1 2 3 4 5 6 7 8 9 10 11 12 13 14 15 16 17 18 19 20 21 22 23 24 25 26 27 28 29 30 31

Goal for Today ....

Food Log	Calories		Protein (g)		Carbs (g)	
	Target ____		Target ____		Target ____	
	Count	Remaining	Count	Remaining	Count	Remaining

You doing ok?   ☺   ☺   ☺   ☹

Tell me about it... ....
....
....

Goal for tomorrow ....

Nutrient Tracker

of Servings   Recommended

Water		
Grains		6 to 8
Veggies		3 to 5
Fruits		2 to 4
Dairy		2 to 3
Protein		3 to 4
Fats	Sugars	Moderation

Jan Feb Mar Apr May June July Aug Sep Oct Nov Dec
1 2 3 4 5 6 7 8 9 10 11 12 13 14 15 16 17 18 19 20 21 22 23 24 25 26 27 28 29 30 31

Goal for Today ....

Food Log	Calories		Protein (g)		Carbs (g)	
	Target ____		Target ____		Target ____	
	Count	Remaining	Count	Remaining	Count	Remaining

You doing ok?   ☺   ☺   ☺   ☹

Tell me about it.... ....
....
....

Goal for tomorrow ....

Nutrient Tracker

of Servings   Recommended

Water		
Grains		6 to 8
Veggies		3 to 5
Fruits		2 to 4
Dairy		2 to 3
Protein		3 to 4
Fats	Sugars	Moderation

Jan   Feb   Mar   Apr   May   June   July   Aug   Sep   Oct   Nov   Dec
1 2 3 4 5 6 7 8 9 10 11 12 13 14 15 16 17 18 19 20 21 22 23 24 25 26 27 28 29 30 31

Goal for Today

Food Log	Calories		Protein (g)		Carbs (g)	
	Target ____		Target ____		Target ____	
	Count	Remaining	Count	Remaining	Count	Remaining

You doing ok?   ☺ ☺ ☺ ☹

Tell me about it...

Goal for tomorrow

Nutrient Tracker

of Servings   Recommended

Water		
Grains		6 to 8
Veggies		3 to 5
Fruits		2 to 4
Dairy		2 to 3
Protein		3 to 4
Fats	Sugars	Moderation

Jan Feb Mar Apr May June July Aug Sep Oct Nov Dec

1 2 3 4 5 6 7 8 9 10 11 12 13 14 15 16 17 18 19 20 21 22 23 24 25 26 27 28 29 30 31

Goal for Today _____

Food Log	Calories Target ____		Protein (g) Target ____		Carbs (g) Target ____	
	Count	Remaining	Count	Remaining	Count	Remaining

You doing ok?   ☺   ☺   ☺   ☹

Tell me about it.... _____

_____

_____

Goal for tomorrow _____

Nutrient Tracker

of Servings   Recommended

Water		
Grains		6 to 8
Veggies		3 to 5
Fruits		2 to 4
Dairy		2 to 3
Protein		3 to 4
Fats	Sugars	Moderation

Jan Feb Mar Apr May June July Aug Sep Oct Nov Dec
1 2 3 4 5 6 7 8 9 10 11 12 13 14 15 16 17 18 19 20 21 22 23 24 25 26 27 28 29 30 31

Goal for Today

Food Log	Calories		Protein (g)		Carbs (g)	
	Target _____		Target _____		Target _____	
	Count	Remaining	Count	Remaining	Count	Remaining

You doing ok?   ☺   ☺   ☺   ☹

Tell me about it...

Goal for tomorrow

Nutrient Tracker

of Servings   Recommended

Water		
Grains		6 to 8
Veggies		3 to 5
Fruits		2 to 4
Dairy		2 to 3
Protein		3 to 4
Fats	Sugars	Moderation

Jan Feb Mar Apr May June July Aug Sep Oct Nov Dec
1 2 3 4 5 6 7 8 9 10 11 12 13 14 15 16 17 18 19 20 21 22 23 24 25 26 27 28 29 30 31

Goal for Today _____

Food Log	Calories Target ____		Protein (g) Target ____		Carbs (g) Target ____	
	Count	Remaining	Count	Remaining	Count	Remaining

You doing ok? ☺ ☺ ☺ ☹

Tell me about it.... _____

Goal for tomorrow _____

Nutrient Tracker

of Servings   Recommended

Water		
Grains		6 to 8
Veggies		3 to 5
Fruits		2 to 4
Dairy		2 to 3
Protein		3 to 4
Fats	Sugars	Moderation

Jan Feb Mar Apr May June July Aug Sep Oct Nov Dec
1 2 3 4 5 6 7 8 9 10 11 12 13 14 15 16 17 18 19 20 21 22 23 24 25 26 27 28 29 30 31

Goal for Today

Food Log	Calories		Protein (g)		Carbs (g)	
	Target ____		Target ____		Target ____	
	Count	Remaining	Count	Remaining	Count	Remaining

You doing ok?   ☺ ☺ ☺ ☹

Tell me about it...

Goal for tomorrow

Nutrient Tracker

of Servings   Recommended

Water		
Grains		6 to 8
Veggies		3 to 5
Fruits		2 to 4
Dairy		2 to 3
Protein		3 to 4
Fats	Sugars	Moderation

Week 2

MY GOAL FOR THE WEEK

HOW I AM GOING TO CELEBRATE

Start where you are. Use what you have. Do what you can.

ARTHUR ASHE

Reflecting on my week

Jan Feb Mar Apr May June July Aug Sep Oct Nov Dec
1 2 3 4 5 6 7 8 9 10 11 12 13 14 15 16 17 18 19 20 21 22 23 24 25 26 27 28 29 30 31

Goal for Today ....

Food Log	Calories		Protein (g)		Carbs (g)	
	Target _____		Target _____		Target _____	
	Count	Remaining	Count	Remaining	Count	Remaining

You doing ok?   ☺ ☺ ☺ ☹

Tell me about it... ....
....
....
....

Goal for tomorrow ....

Nutrient Tracker

of Servings   Recommended

Water		
Grains		6 to 8
Veggies		3 to 5
Fruits		2 to 4
Dairy		2 to 3
Protein		3 to 4
Fats	Sugars	Moderation

Jan   Feb   Mar   Apr   May   June   July   Aug   Sep   Oct   Nov   Dec
1 2 3 4 5 6 7 8 9 10 11 12 13 14 15 16 17 18 19 20 21 22 23 24 25 26 27 28 29 30 31

Goal for Today _____

Food Log	Calories		Protein (g)		Carbs (g)	
	Target ____		Target ____		Target ____	
	Count	Remaining	Count	Remaining	Count	Remaining

You doing ok?   ☺ ☺ ☹ ☹

Tell me about it.... _____

_____

_____

Goal for tomorrow _____

Nutrient Tracker

of Servings   Recommended

Water		
Grains		6 to 8
Veggies		3 to 5
Fruits		2 to 4
Dairy		2 to 3
Protein		3 to 4
Fats	Sugars	Moderation

Jan Feb Mar Apr May June July Aug Sep Oct Nov Dec
1 2 3 4 5 6 7 8 9 10 11 12 13 14 15 16 17 18 19 20 21 22 23 24 25 26 27 28 29 30 31

Goal for Today ....

Food Log	Calories Target _____		Protein (g) Target _____		Carbs (g) Target _____	
	Count	Remaining	Count	Remaining	Count	Remaining

You doing ok?   ☺ ☺ ☺ ☹

Tell me about it... ....
....
....
Goal for tomorrow ....

Nutrient Tracker

of Servings   Recommended

Water		
Grains		6 to 8
Veggies		3 to 5
Fruits		2 to 4
Dairy		2 to 3
Protein		3 to 4
Fats	Sugars	Moderation

Jan   Feb   Mar   Apr   May   June   July   Aug   Sep   Oct   Nov   Dec
1 2 3 4 5 6 7 8 9 10 11 12 13 14 15 16 17 18 19 20 21 22 23 24 25 26 27 28 29 30 31

Goal for Today _____

Food Log	Calories		Protein (g)		Carbs (g)	
	Target ____		Target ____		Target ____	
	Count	Remaining	Count	Remaining	Count	Remaining

You doing ok?   ☺   ☺   ☹   ☹

Tell me about it.... _____
_____
_____

Goal for tomorrow _____

Nutrient Tracker

of Servings   Recommended

		Recommended
Water		
Grains		6 to 8
Veggies		3 to 5
Fruits		2 to 4
Dairy		2 to 3
Protein		3 to 4
Fats	Sugars	Moderation

Jan   Feb   Mar   Apr   May   June   July   Aug   Sep   Oct   Nov   Dec
1 2 3 4 5 6 7 8 9 10 11 12 13 14 15 16 17 18 19 20 21 22 23 24 25 26 27 28 29 30 31

Goal for Today

Food Log	Calories		Protein (g)		Carbs (g)	
	Target ____		Target ____		Target ____	
	Count	Remaining	Count	Remaining	Count	Remaining

You doing ok?   ☺   ☺   ☹   ☹

Tell me about it...

Goal for tomorrow

Nutrient Tracker

of Servings   Recommended

Water		
Grains		6 to 8
Veggies		3 to 5
Fruits		2 to 4
Dairy		2 to 3
Protein		3 to 4
Fats	Sugars	Moderation

Jan   Feb   Mar   Apr   May   June   July   Aug   Sep   Oct   Nov   Dec
1 2 3 4 5 6 7 8 9 10 11 12 13 14 15 16 17 18 19 20 21 22 23 24 25 26 27 28 29 30 31

Goal for Today _____

Food Log	Calories		Protein (g)		Carbs (g)	
	Target ____		Target ____		Target ____	
	Count	Remaining	Count	Remaining	Count	Remaining

You doing ok?   ☺ ☺ ☺ ☹

Tell me about it.... _____
_____
_____

Goal for tomorrow   _____

Nutrient Tracker

of Servings   Recommended

Water		
Grains		6 to 8
Veggies		3 to 5
Fruits		2 to 4
Dairy		2 to 3
Protein		3 to 4
Fats	Sugars	Moderation

Jan   Feb   Mar   Apr   May   June   July   Aug   Sep   Oct   Nov   Dec
1 2 3 4 5 6 7 8 9 10 11 12 13 14 15 16 17 18 19 20 21 22 23 24 25 26 27 28 29 30 31

Goal for Today _____

Food Log	Calories		Protein (g)		Carbs (g)	
	Target ____		Target ____		Target ____	
	Count	Remaining	Count	Remaining	Count	Remaining

You doing ok? ☺ ☺ ☺ ☹

Tell me about it... _____
_____
_____

Goal for tomorrow _____

Nutrient Tracker

of Servings   Recommended

Water		
Grains		6 to 8
Veggies		3 to 5
Fruits		2 to 4
Dairy		2 to 3
Protein		3 to 4
Fats	Sugars	Moderation

Week 1

MY GOAL FOR THE WEEK

HOW I AM GOING TO CELEBRATE

Food